MIMI the MONARCH

A Butterfly's Transformation on Mackinac Island

by Mark & Natalia Wohletz

Mackinac Memories, llc.

FOR MIMI – Mark & Natalia

MIMI the MONARCH
A Butterfly's Transformation on Mackinac Island

"Mimi the Monarch" was inspired by Natalia's field study on monarchs and their Mackinac Island, Mich., habitats during the summer of 2016. She conducted the study for her Kalamazoo College Senior Individual Project and the Mackinac State Historic Parks.

Story by Mark Wohletz
Field Notes & Sketches by Natalia Wohletz
Edited by Sue Allen
Subject Matter Review by Ilse Gebhard, Monarch Larva Monitoring Project, Volunteer
Photography & Design by Jennifer Wohletz

Contributing Photographers: Natalia Wohletz (p. 20, 28-29), Dan Wohletz (p. 4, bridge top, 22, 42), Shutterstock.com/Jacob Hamblin (46, flying monarch), Shutterstock.com/Elizaveta Kirina (p. 46-47, roosting monarchs), Annie Lockwood (p. 48), Shutterstock.com/cicloco (p. 54, monarch pair), Shutterstock/julee75 (p. 54, emerging butterfly), Max Jones (p. 56, Mark)

Published by Mackinac Memories, llc. | www.mackinacislandmemories.com | mackinacmemoriesllc@gmail.com
P.O. Box 1586, Mackinac Island, MI 49757 (seasonal) | 4189 Stison Crest Court, White Lake, MI 48383
For every book sold, Mackinac Memories, llc. will make a donation to the Mackinac Island Community Foundation.

Printed in the USA
Library of Congress: 2017905644 | ISBN-13: 978-0-9973847-3-4 | ISBN-10: 0-9973847-3-5

"*Happiness is like a butterfly:*
the more you chase it, the more it will elude you,
but if you turn your attention to other things,
it will come and sit softly on your shoulder."

– Henry David Thoreau

Mama Monarch's on a mission

She doesn't drift and roam.

She flies over the Mighty Mac

Searching for a perfect home.

Field Notes:

Each spring, the monarch butterfly population begins a slow journey north from Mexico to the northern United States of America and southern Canada. The overwintering generation stops to mate and lay eggs in Texas and other southern states. Then their offspring continue the journey until they, too, stop to lay eggs and let the next generation take their place. Sometimes a monarch butterfly will fly more than 250 miles in one day!

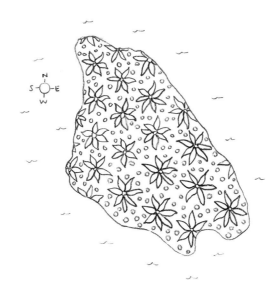

Mama Monarch wants to find

A meadow green and grand.

A great place to start her family

On Mackinac Island she will land.

Field Notes:

Some monarch butterflies choose Mackinac Island, Mich., as their northern home because they are attracted to the milkweed and blooming flowers growing in meadows and gardens.

Mama Monarch knows there's nectar

In the flowers blooming pink.

She knows the plants are special

They make food for her to drink.

Field Notes:

Flowers provide monarchs with the food they need to be healthy. The butterflies are not picky eaters and like to eat nectar from flowers of almost every color.

Mama Monarch sips some nectar.

Then spots her mate up in a tree.

He spreads his wings, white, orange and black.

A beautiful sight to see.

Field Notes:

A female monarch needs a male partner to fertilize her eggs before she can lay them. You can tell a monarch's gender by its wings. Female monarchs have thicker wing veins (the black lines separating the orange shapes), while males have thin wing veins and black spots on the lower wings.

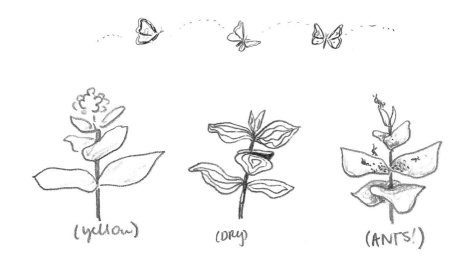

(yellow)   (DRY)   (ANTS!)

Mama Monarch knows it's time

To lay eggs on a milkweed plant.

But some are yellow. Some are dry.

And some are full of ANTS!

Field Notes:

Female monarchs lay eggs on milkweed plants because their caterpillars are picky eaters: They only eat milkweed leaves. If she has a choice, a monarch butterfly will choose green, soft and healthy milkweed and avoid plants that are yellow, dry or have ants and aphids. Ants are most dangerous to monarchs when they are guarding tiny insects called aphids that live on milkweed plants. They will attack anything (including humans!) that bother the aphids.

(Just right)

Mama Monarch sees a healthy plant
In a meadow long and wide,
There's green and yummy milkweed leaves
That her babies need to thrive.

Mama Monarch lays her egg

On a milkweed's underside.

She glues the egg where it is safe

From hungry, prying eyes.

Field Notes:
Female monarchs can lay 300-500 eggs in the wild, but only about 30-50 (10 percent) survive to become butterflies. She typically lays eggs one at a time on the bottom of a leaf near the top of the milkweed plant. Her goal is to shelter the egg from the sun, rain and hungry, flying predators.

At last the egg breaks open

Baby Monarch creeps outside.

She eats the shell and looks around

For food and a place to hide.

Field Notes:

A caterpillar hatches from its egg after about three to seven days, then eats the eggshell before nibbling on the topmost layer of a milkweed leaf. Young monarch caterpillars must be careful to not bite all the way into the leaf because milkweed plants contain a sticky, milky-looking substance called latex that may ooze out and glue them to the spot. Plus, if they take a bite of the latex, their mouthparts become sticky making it difficult to eat.

Baby Monarch keeps on growing

Sporting stripes along her back.

Yellow, black and white lines

Warn she's NOT a tasty snack.

Field Notes:

As a caterpillar gets bigger it can take larger bites out of milkweed leaves. At this stage, the milkweed latex is actually good for the monarchs because it makes them poisonous to predators. As a caterpillar grows, yellow stripes emerge on its back. The yellow warns predators to stay away.

Baby Monarch meets lots of bugs
Some are nice and some are scary.
Big white spiders want to eat her
So she must be very wary.

Baby Monarch is growing fast.

She needs milkweed to get strong.

She's climbing, creeping all around

And eating all day long.

Field Notes:
A monarch caterpillar grows from 2 mm to 45 mm (1.77 inches) in a surprisingly short time span: 10-14 days. It can eat the equivalent of one whole milkweed plant during its development!

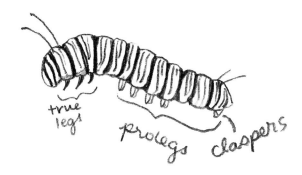

true legs

prolegs claspers

Baby Monarch has six legs

And claspers help her creep.

She moves around from plant to plant

And stays in place while she's asleep.

Field Notes:

As the caterpillar grows, it becomes too big for its skin and sheds it like a snake before eating the skin as a snack. This process is called molting and the time in between is referred to as instars. The caterpillar will molt five times before transforming into a chrysalis.

Baby Monarch is now big and fat

It's time to make her move.

She explores a field with her friends,

Mama Monarch would approve.

One friend finds a wooden fence

He climbs up to the top.

He makes a pad of silky glue

And he sticks right to the spot.

Another finds a pretty plant

It's a lovely place to stay.

She sticks her legs upon a leaf

Then hangs there like a "J."

Field Notes:

Once they are big enough, monarch caterpillars move away from their home plant in search of a sturdy, safe place to transform into a chyrsalis. On the underside of a fence, bench or strong leaf, the full-grown caterpillars create a pad of sticky silk, then grab the silk with their back legs called claspers and hang upside down in a "J" shape. Then they shed their skin for the last time and turn into a bright green chrysalis with gold spots.

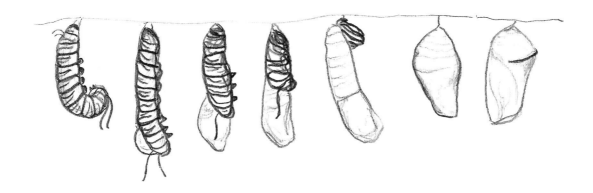

Baby Monarch takes a major step

There is a lot to gain.

She transforms into a chrysalis

Protected from the rain.

Field Notes:

The monarch stays in the green chrysalis with gold spots for about 9 to 15 days. Scientists think the color is for camouflage, though no one knows for sure. Although their adult body parts, including legs, wings, antennae, proboscis, and more start growing during the caterpillar stage, they must become a chrysalis before they can completely develop into a butterfly.

The chrysalis is strong and hard

A peaceful place to be.

As painted wings begin to grow

She can't wait for all to see.

Field Notes:

In time, the butterfly's developing wings can be seen through the filmy outer layer of the chrysalis case. Inside, a metamorphosis is taking place and soon a butterfly will emerge.

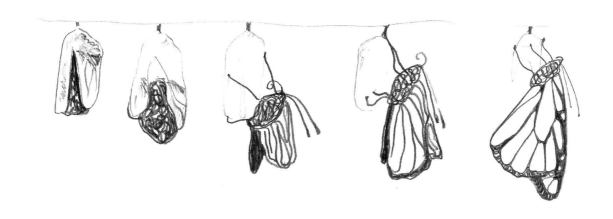

Baby Monarch breaks out from her case,

MIMI is her name.

She flaps her wings, black, orange and white.

They are her claim to fame.

Field Notes:

Once the adult body parts are fully developed, the monarch breaks through the casing and emerges into the open with shriveled wings. The butterfly begins pumping fluid from its abdomen to expand its wings. After about three to four hours, the butterfly spreads its wings and flies away.

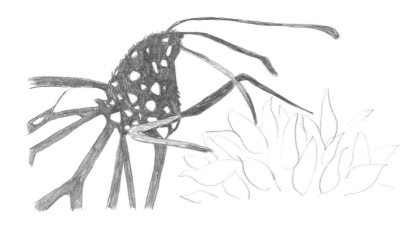

Mimi the Monarch drinks some nectar

With her tongue that's like a straw.

She moves around from plant to plant

In her home on Mackinac.

Field Notes:

When an adult monarch lands on a flower, it unravels its proboscis, a flexible tongue-like mouthpart shaped like a tube. The monarch sips nectar up through its proboscis just like people sip drinks through a straw.

Mimi the Monarch flits and flutters

She stops to drink along the way.

She's preparing for a journey

To a place far, far away.

Field Notes:
Monarchs born in the northern migration range in late summer and early fall do not continue the journey north. Instead, they migrate south to spend the winter in Central Mexico.

Mimi the Monarch knows it's time,

For her migration to begin.

She sets her course. She's flying south.

To spend winter with her kin.

Field Notes:

The journey south to Mexico from Mackinac Island, Mich., is over 2,000 miles long, so the monarchs fly and eat during the day, then roost (rest) in trees overnight. Some monarchs also spend the winter in Florida and California, depending on their migration route.

Mimi the Monarch flies until
She meets her friends in Mexico.
They're resting in a forest
Where her family likes to go.

Mimi the Monarch spends the winter

Resting and waiting for her cue.

She'll start her northbound journey

In the spring when skies are blue.

Field Notes:

During the winter, monarchs remain mostly inactive, resting in the cooler weather. On warm days, they may flutter around to find water to drink, but they eat enough on the migration south that they do not need to eat much in the winter. They roost in tall trees that shelter them from predators, rain, snow and unsafe temperatures.

While Mimi the Monarch rests down south

The milkweed goes to seed.

Mother Nature's getting ready

To grow food that monarchs need.

THE END (or just the beginning)

Field Notes:

There are about 130 different milkweed species native to North America. Planting milkweed in landscaped gardens, naturalized meadows and roadside fields is an easy way to create healthy habitats for monarchs.

"The charismatic monarch butterfly is an irreplaceable piece of the natural history of North America. Yet this butterfly, that was once common across the country, is now plummeting toward extinction and needs protection or is at risk of being lost forever.

"No other butterfly species on Earth undertakes a migration like the North American monarch. The multi-generational migration of the monarch butterfly can cover thousands of miles and is often described as spectacular, mysterious, and extraordinary."

– Petition to Protect the Monarch Butterfly Under the Endangered Species Act, (Submitted Aug. 26, 2014 before the Secretary of the Interior)

A naturalized garden of native milkweed along British Landing Road, Mackinac Island, Mich.

HOW TO HELP MONARCH BUTTERFLIES

Due to the monarch butterfly's enormous habitat range, conservation is a continent-wide issue. There are two easy ways to get involved and help monarchs thrive: Plant a butterfly garden and join a citizen science program.

Plant a Butterfly Garden

All monarchs truly need is milkweed plants and flowers full of nectar for food. A good butterfly garden has both and is never treated with pesticides. When considering the type of milkweed, consult an expert at your local plant nursery or visit www.xerces.org/milkweed-seed-finder/ to find milkweeds native to your area. Native flowering plants are also best for providing the nectar they need for fuel. To determine which flowering plants are native to your region and attract butterflies, ask an expert at your local plant greenhouse or visit www.pollinator.org/guides.

Join a Citizen Science Program

Also consider joining a citizen science program to help track and monitor the monarch butterfly population. A few examples of citizen science programs include Journey North, Monarch Watch and the Monarch Larva Monitoring Project.

Journey North tracks the spring and fall migration of monarch butterflies through reports of monarch sightings. The Monarch Larva Monitoring Project records monarch egg, larvae, pupae and adult counts throughout the breeding season. Monarch Watch tags monarchs in the fall to determine fall migration routes.

For more information on these opportunities and others, visit www.monarchjointventure.org/get-involved/study-monarchs-citizen-science-opportunities.

"Monarchs' needs are simple. They need milkweed and nectar sources in areas that are not treated with insecticides. So any landscaping you can do that includes these needs will help monarchs."

– Dr. Karen Oberhauser
College of Biological Sciences
Unversity of Minnesota

LEARNING RESOURCES

There's lots to learn about monarchs and wonderful resources to tap for information. Here are a few sources:
The Monarch Migration by Dr. Lincoln Brower
www.youtube.com/watch?v=tTGCjYCrYf4
www.monarchconservation.org
www.monarchwatch.org
www.xerces.org
www.monarchlab.org
www.journeynorth.org/monarch/
www.monarchjointventure.org
www.monarchmentors.org
www.nwf.org
www.wildones.org
www.makewayformonarchs.org
www.pollinator.org/guides

A monarch on a wildflower in a meadow.

MONARCH LIFE CYCLE

The monarch butterfly's life cycle begins as an egg. Upon hatching, the monarch caterpillar goes through five stages, or "instars," of growth, each ending in molting of the skin. After the final instar, the caterpillar hangs upside down in a "J" shape and transforms into a chrysalis. About one week later, the monarch emerges from its chrysalis as a butterfly.

GLOSSARY

Chrysalis – the pupal developmental stage of a butterfly when caterpillars become butterflies

Pesticide – chemical used to kill insects

Kin – a person's family and/or relations

Journey – a trip; period of travel

Mackinac Island – an island in the Great Lakes between the two peninsulas of Michigan

Mate – a reproductive partner

Meadow – a field of grasses and flowers

Metamorphosis – a complete change in form from egg to caterpillar to pupa to butterfly

Mighty Mac – the Mackinac Bridge connects Michigan's Upper and Lower Peninsulas

Migration – seasonal movement of animals across regions

Mission – an important goal or task

Milkweed – a genus of plants native to North America, most of which release a milky latex

Monarch – a butterfly native to North America

Native – belonging or having ancestral roots to a region

Nectar – sugary liquid in flowers to attract pollinators

Proboscis – tube-like mouthpiece of insects

Pupa – a monarch in the inactive stage of development as a chrysalis

Overwinter – to remain in a place for the winter

Roosting – to perch or rest somewhere

Thrive – to grow, develop or be successful

Transformation – the process of changing form, shape, appearance or nature

MACKINAC ISLAND

Mackinac Island, Mich., is located in the Great Lakes where the waters of Lakes Huron and Michigan meet. Just like monarchs, many people travel to the island each summer to experience its beautiful scenery and natural environment. The island is best known for its rich history and unique horse culture. Motorized vehicles are banned so visitors and residents alike enjoy hiking and riding bikes, saddle horses or horse-drawn carriages to get around. Along with American history, visitors have an opportunity to learn about the magical metamorphosis of butterflies thanks to beautiful displays at The Original Butterfly House and Wings of Mackinac.

BIBLIOGRAPHY

Flockhart, D.T.T., Pichancourt, J., Norris, D.R., Martin, T.G. 2015. Unravelling the annual cycle in a migratory animal: breeding-season habitat loss drives population declines of monarch butterflies. J. Anim. Eco. 84: 155-165.

Fuentes, T. Migrating Monarchs [Internet]. 2017 [cited 2017 March 20]. Ask A Biologist. Available from https://askabiologist.asu.edu/explore/migrating-monarch

Landis, T.D. 2014. Monarch waystations: propagating native plants to create travel corridors for migrating monarch butterflies. J. Native Plants. 15(1): 4-16.

Luna, T., Dumroese, R.K. 2013. Monarchs (Danaus plexippus) and milkweeds (Asclepias species): the current situation and methods for propagating milkweeds. J. Native Plants. 14(1): 4-15.

Oberhauser, K.S. 2004. Overview of monarch breeding biology. In: The Monarch Butterfly: Biology and Conservation. (Oberhauser, K.S, Solensky, M.J., eds.). Cornell University Press, NY, pp. 3-8.

Oberhauser, K.S. Answers from the Monarch Butterfly Expert Spring 2014. [Internet]. 2014 [cited 2017 March 20]. Journey North. Available from https://www.learner.org/jnorth/tm/monarch/ExpertAnswer14.html

Oberhauser, K.S., and Luda, K.. 1997. A Field Guide to Monarch Caterpillars, University of Minnesota.

Prysby, M.D. 2004. Natural enemies and survival of monarch eggs and larvae. In: The Monarch Butterfly: Biology and Conservation. (Oberhauser, K.S, Solensky, M.J., eds.). Cornell University Press, NY, pp. 27-37.

Pleasants, J.M., Oberhauser, K.S. 2013. Milkweed loss in agricultural fields because of herbicide use: effect on the monarch butterfly population. Insect Conservation and Diversity 6(2): 135-144.

University of Minnesota Monarch Lab. Frequently asked questions: monarch biology. [Internet]. 2016 [cited 2016 October 27]. University of Minnesota Monarch Lab: Biology and Research. Available from http://monarchlab.org/biology-and-research/ask-the-expert/faq/

The Center for Biological Diversity, Center for Food Safety, The Xerces Society, and Lincoln Brower. "Petition to Protect the Monarch Butterfly (Danaus Plexippus Plexippus) Under the Endangered Spieces Act." The Xerces Society. N.p., 2014. Web.

Field Notes Author & Illustrator

Natalia Wohletz and her dog, Johan, were a common sight in the milkweed patches of Mackinac Island during the summer of 2016. The island resident studied the world of monarchs – counting, measuring and documenting what she encountered. Natalia is a Kalamazoo College graduate with a BA in mathematics, minor in studio arts and concentration in environmental studies. She strongly supports conservation and hopes this book creates awareness of monarchs and helps all endangered pollinators thrive.

MIMI the MONARCH

Our monarch is named "MIMI" to represent **Mackinac Island, MI**. The name is also in honor of two special women in our lives: Mimi (Georgette) Sorrentino and Mimi (Maril) McHale.

The Story Author

Mark Wohletz joined forces with his sister, Natalia, to share the story of a monarch's transformation on Mackinac Island because he was inspired by the photographs of the monarch caterpillars and butterflies featured in her field study. His goal is to raise awareness of the need for milkweed habitats across the USA and Mexico. Mark is a full-time student at the International Academy West in Metro Detroit and summer bike mechanic at Mackinac Wheels. His poetry has been published by the American Library of Poetry.

ACKNOWLEDGEMENTS

Special thanks to subject matter experts Ilse Gebhard of the Monarch Larva Monitoring Project and Marie Hulett of Wings of Mackinac for their fact-checking reviews. Dr. E. Binney Girdler of Kalamazoo College, Jeff Dykehouse and Phil Porter of the Mackinac State Historic Parks for supporting Natalia's 2016 monarch field study. Sue Allen for her editorial review. Emory Barnwell, Abby Brenz, Ian McGreevy and Olivia Meszaros for their help with the field study. Dr. Stephen Humphrey, Lin Sheppard, Trish Martin, Maeve Croghan, Allison Sehoyan, Ruth Adamus and Debby Cummings for their support and interest in monarchs. Mary, Barry and Carrie Kluczyk for their tips on story content. Mary Jane Barnwell of The Island Bookstore for her encouragement. Dr. Karen Oberhauser of the University of Minnesota, for her vast research on monarchs, which Natalia referenced for her study and this book.

Jennifer Wohletz for her photographs capturing monarchs in all stages of metamorphosis during the summer of 2016. Dan Wohletz for the images of a big white spider and a monarch sipping nectar in his island backyard. Annie Lockwood for hiking two miles up steep, rocky terrain into the Piedra Herrada Reserve in Mexico to snap the images of monarchs roosting. Perhaps some of the monarchs in her photos migrated from Mackinac Island, Michigan!